The Puffin Mother Goose Treasury

RAYMOND BRIGGS

PUFFIN

For Jean

The rhymes are reproduced with acknowledgements

and grateful thanks to Peter and Iona Opie

PUFFIN BOOKS
Published by the Penguin Group: London, New York, Australia,
Canada, India, Ireland, New Zealand and South Africa
Penguin Books Ltd, Registered Offices: 80 Strand,
London WC2R 0RL, England

puffinbooks.com

First published by Hamish Hamilton as *The Mother Goose Treasury* 1966
Published in Picture Puffins 1973
This abridged edition published 2010
1 3 5 7 9 10 8 6 4 2
Copyright © Raymond Briggs, 1966
The moral right of the author/illustrator has been asserted
Made and printed in China
ISBN: 978-0-141-32966-6

A few words from Raymond Briggs

Treasury is a good word for it.

Nursery rhymes are a national treasure.

All human life is here: birth, love, marriage and death. Underneath their jolly, rollicking rhythms and rhymes there is a depth and a truth about life.

They also have surreal, crazy humour, quiet philosophy, wisdom, lunatic nonsense and subtle poetry. There is no finer field for the illustrator. The only other texts that come near it are fairy tales. They are wonderful too, but there is usually less humour, nonsense and craziness. Nursery rhymes also have the rhythms of counting games, chants and songs.

The verses live on in our memories for the whole of our lives. Who can ever forget Hey diddle, diddle, the cat and the fiddle? Humpty Dumpty had a great fall. Hush-a-bye baby, on the tree top, When the wind blows . . . We all absorbed these words in our cradles, both as games and lullabies. They become part of us forever.

Nursery Rhymes is perhaps not the best title for these verses and songs. There is nothing pretty-pretty, pink and blue, babyish about them. They seem to come from the world of peasants, farmers and the labouring poor. They are rough, tough and earthy, sometimes blunt, violent and very matter-of-fact about the harder things in life. A better title might be Folk Poetry, but that is not right either. It may be that Mother Goose Rhymes is perhaps the best after all, because these verses are not classifiable. Like life itself, they cannot be sorted into a labelled box, they are universal and, because they are universal, have endured over the years.

It was wonderful, back in 1964, to be offered this amazing job. The editor wanted it to be the biggest colour-illustrated Mother Goose ever, and it still is today. There are over 800 illustrations and this was a mammoth task. It took over two years and I was paid a monthly fee of £83. 6s. 8d. to keep me alive whilst working on it. I was still alive at the end, just, and still more or less sane, I think. Nevertheless, it was a great privilege to be asked to undertake this monumental work, and it was very enjoyable to do . . . Then, for the book to be awarded the Library Association's Kate Greenaway for 1966 was a great honour. Now, for Puffin to re-publish it on their 70th Anniversary, over 40 years later, is another reward in itself.

But, I just wish they had kept up the £83. 6s. 8d per month for the last 45 years.

CONTENTS

Old Mother Goose and the Golden Egg

Old Mother Goose,
When she wanted to wander,
Would ride through the air
On a very fine gander.

Mother Goose had a house,
'Twas built in a wood,
Where an owl at the door
For sentinel stood.

She had a son Jack,
A plain-looking lad,
He was not very good,
Nor yet very bad.

She sent him to market,
A live goose he bought;
See, Mother, says he,
I have not been for nought.

Jack's goose and her gander
Grew very fond;
They'd both eat together,
Or swim in the pond.

Jack found one fine morning,
As I have been told,
His goose had laid him
An egg of pure gold.

Jack ran to his mother
The news for to tell,
She called him a good boy,
And said it was well.

Jack sold his gold egg
To a merchant untrue,
Who cheated him out of
A half of his due.

Then Jack went a-courting
A lady so gay,
As fair as the lily,
And sweet as the May.

The merchant and squire
Soon came at his back,
And began to belabour
The sides of poor Jack.

Then old Mother Goose
That instant came in,
And turned her son Jack
Into famed Harlequin.

She then with her wand
Touched the lady so fine,
And turned her at once
Into sweet Columbine.

The gold egg in the sea
Was thrown away then,
When an odd fish brought her
The egg back again.

The merchant then vowed
The goose he would kill,
Resolving at once
His pockets to fill.

Jack's mother came in,
And caught the goose soon,
And mounting its back,
Flew up to the moon.

Bobby Shaftoe

Bobby Shaftoe's gone to sea,
Silver buckles at his knee;
He'll come back and marry me,
Bonny Bobby Shaftoe.

Bobby Shaftoe's bright and fair,
Combing down his yellow hair,
He's my ain for evermair,
Bonny Bobby Shaftoe.

Bobby Shaftoe's tall and slim,
He's always dressed so neat and trim,
The ladies they all keek at him,
Bonny Bobby Shaftoe.

Bobby Shaftoe's getten a bairn
For to dandle in his arm;
In his arm and on his knee,
Bobby Shaftoe loves me.

Pat-a-Cake

Pat-a-cake, pat-a-cake, baker's man,
Bake me a cake as fast as you can;
Pat it and prick it, and mark it with T,
Put it in the oven for Tommy and me.

Old Mother Hubbard and her Dog

Old Mother Hubbard
Went to the cupboard,
To fetch her poor dog a bone;
But when she got there
The cupboard was bare
And so the poor dog had none.

She went to the baker's
To buy him some bread;
But when she came back
The poor dog was dead.

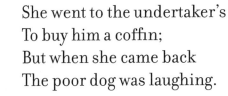

She went to the undertaker's
To buy him a coffin;
But when she came back
The poor dog was laughing.

She took a clean dish
To get him some tripe;
But when she came back
He was smoking a pipe.

She went to the fishmonger's
To buy him some fish;
But when she came back
He was licking the dish.

She went to the tavern
For white wine and red;
But when she came back
The dog stood on his head.

She went to the fruiterer's
To buy him some fruit;
But when she came back
He was playing the flute.

She went to the tailor's
To buy him a coat;
But when she came back
He was riding a goat.

She went to the hatter's
To buy him a hat;
But when she came back
He was feeding the cat.

She went to the barber's
To buy him a wig;
But when she came back
He was dancing a jig.

She went to the cobbler's
To buy him some shoes;
But when she came back
He was reading the news.

She went to the seamstress
To buy him some linen;
But when she came back
The dog was a-spinning.

She went to the hosier's
To buy him some hose;
But when she came back
He was dressed in his clothes.

The dame made a curtsey,
The dog made a bow;
The dame said, Your servant,
The dog said, Bow-wow.

You Shall be Queen

Lilies are white,
Rosemary's green,
When I am king,
You shall be queen.

Little Blue Ben

Little Blue Ben, who lives in the glen,
Keeps a blue cat and one blue hen,
Which lays of blue eggs a score and ten;
Where shall I find the little Blue Ben?

Baa, Baa, Black Sheep

Baa, baa, black sheep,
Have you any wool?
Yes, sir, yes, sir,
Three bags full;
One for the master,
And one for the dame,
And one for the little boy
Who lives down the lane.

Sing a Song of Sixpence

Sing a song of sixpence,
A pocket full of rye;
Four and twenty blackbirds,
Baked in a pie.

When the pie was opened,
The birds began to sing;
Was not that a dainty dish,
To set before a king?

The king was in his counting-house,
Counting out his money;
The queen was in the parlour
Eating bread and honey.

The maid was in the garden,
Hanging out the clothes,
When down came a blackbird
And pecked off her nose.

Rain Before Seven

Rain before seven,
Fine before eleven.

Incey Wincey

Incey Wincey spider
Climbing up the spout;
Down came the rain
And washed the spider out;
Out came the sunshine
And dried up all the rain;
Incey Wincey spider
Climbing up again.

The Crooked Man

There was a crooked man,
And he walked a crooked mile,
He found a crooked sixpence
Against a crooked stile;
He bought a crooked cat,
Which caught a crooked mouse,
And they all lived together
In a little crooked house.

Wibbleton and Wobbleton

From Wibbleton to Wobbleton is
    fifteen miles,
From Wobbleton to Wibbleton is
    fifteen miles,
From Wibbleton to Wobbleton,
From Wobbleton to Wibbleton,
From Wibbleton to Wobbleton is
    fifteen miles.

Queen Caroline

Queen, Queen Caroline,
Washed her hair in turpentine,
Turpentine to make it shine,
Queen, Queen Caroline.

Old Farmer Giles

Old Farmer Giles,
    He went seven miles
With his faithful dog Old Rover;
    And Old Farmer Giles,
    When he came to the stiles,
Took a run, and jumped clean over.

Terence McDiddler

Terence McDiddler,
The three-fingered fiddler,
Can charm, if you please,
The fish from the seas.

Boy Blue

Little Boy Blue,
Come blow your horn,
The sheep's in the meadow,
The cow's in the corn.
Where is the boy
Who looks after the sheep?
He's under a haystack
Fast asleep.
Will you wake him?
No, not I,
For if I do,
He's sure to cry.

Red Stockings

Red stockings, blue stockings,
Shoes tied up with silver;
A red rosette upon my breast
And a gold ring on my finger.

| MON | TUE | WED | THUR | FRI | SAT | SUN |

A Week of Birthdays

Monday's child
   is fair of face,
Tuesday's child
   is full of grace,
Wednesday's child
   is full of woe,
Thursday's child
   has far to go,
Friday's child
   is loving and giving,
Saturday's child
   works hard for its living,
But the child that's born
   on the Sabbath day
Is bonny and blithe,
   and good and gay.

Sea Shells

She sells sea-shells on the sea shore;
The shells that she sells are sea-shells I'm sure.
So if she sells sea-shells on the sea shore,
I'm sure that the shells are sea-shore shells.

The Rugged Rock

Round and round the rugged rock
The ragged rascal ran.
How many R's are there in that?
Now tell me if you can.

Missing Commas I

I saw a peacock with a fiery tail
I saw a blazing comet drop down hail
I saw a cloud with ivy curled around
I saw a sturdy oak creep on the ground
I saw an ant swallow up a whale
I saw a raging sea brim full of ale
I saw a Venice glass sixteen foot deep
I saw a well full of men's tears that weep
I saw their eyes all in a flame of fire
I saw a house high as the moon and higher
I saw the sun at twelve o'clock at night
I saw the man who saw this wondrous sight.

The North Wind

The north wind doth blow,
And we shall have snow,
And what will poor Robin do then,
    Poor thing?
He'll sit in a barn,
And keep himself warm,
And hide his head under his wing,
    Poor thing.

To the Cuckoo

Cuckoo, cuckoo, what do you do?
In April I open my bill;
In May I sing all day;
In June I change my tune;
In July away I fly;
In August away I must.

Jeremiah Obadiah

Jeremiah Obadiah, puff, puff, puff.
When he gives his messages he snuffs, snuffs, snuffs,
When he goes to school by day, he roars, roars, roars,
When he goes to bed at night he snores, snores, snores,
When he goes to Christmas treat he eats plum-duff,
Jeremiah Obadiah, puff, puff, puff.

Goosey Gander

Goosey, goosey gander,
  Wither shall I wander?
Upstairs and downstairs
  And in my lady's chamber.
There I met an old man
  Who would not say his prayers,
I took him by the left leg
  And threw him down the stairs.

Three Jovial Welshmen

There were three jovial Welshmen,
  As I have heard men say,
And they would go a-hunting
  Upon St David's Day.

All the day they hunted
  And nothing could they find,
But a ship a-sailing,
  A-sailing with the wind.

One said it was a ship,
  The other he said, Nay;
The third said it was a house,
  With the chimney blown away.

And all the night they hunted
  And nothing could they find,
But the moon a-gliding,
  A-gliding with the wind.

One said it was the moon,
  The other he said, Nay;
The third said it was a cheese,
  And half of it cut away.

And all the day they hunted
  And nothing could they find,
But a hedgehog in a bramble bush,
  And that they left behind.

The first said it was a hedgehog,
  The second he said, Nay;
The third said it was a pincushion,
  And the pins stuck in wrong way.

And all the night they hunted
  And nothing could they find,
But a hare in a turnip field,
  And that they left behind.

The first said it was a hare,
  The second he said, Nay;
The third said it was a calf,
  And the cow had run away.

And all the day they hunted
  And nothing could they find,
But an owl in a holly tree,
  And that they left behind.

One said it was an owl,
  The other he said, Nay;
The third said 'twas an old man,
  And his beard growing grey.

The Star

Twinkle, twinkle, little star,
How I wonder what you are!
Up above the world so high,
Like a diamond in the sky.

A Rat

There was a rat, for want of stairs,
Went down a rope to say his prayers.

The Grand Old Duke of York

Oh, the grand old Duke of York,
He had ten thousand men;
He marched them up to the top of the hill,
And he marched them down again.
And when they were up, they were up,
And when they were down, they were down,
And when they were only half way up,
They were neither up nor down.

Charlie Warlie

Charlie Warlie had a cow,
Black and white about the brow;
Open the gate and let her through,
Charlie Warlie's old cow.

The Giant

Fee, fi, fo, fum,
I smell the blood of an Englishman:
Be he alive or be he dead,
I'll grind his bones to make my bread.

Corporal Bill

Here's Corporal Bull
A strong hearty fellow,
Who not used to fighting
Set up a loud bellow.

Goose Feathers

Cackle, cackle, Mother Goose,
Have you any feathers loose?
Truly have I, pretty fellow,
Half enough to fill a pillow.
Here are quills, take one or two,
And down to make a bed for you.

King of the Castle

I'm the king of the castle,
Get down you dirty rascal.

Pick-a-Back

Matthew, Mark, Luke, and John,
Hold my horse till I leap on,
Hold him steady, hold him sure,
And I'll get over the misty moor.

See-Saw

See-saw, Margery Daw,
Jacky shall have a new master;
Jacky shall have but a penny a day,
Because he can't work any faster.

One, Two, Three, Four, Five

One, two, three, four, five,
Once I caught a fish alive,
Six, seven, eight, nine, ten,
Then I let it go again.
Why did you let it go?
Because it bit my finger so.
Which finger did it bite?
The little finger on the right.

My Little Dog

Oh where, oh where has my little dog gone?
   Oh where, oh where can he be?
With his ears cut short and his tail cut long,
   Oh where, oh where is he?

The House That Jack Built

This is the house
    that Jack built.

This is the malt
That lay in the house
    that Jack built.

This is the rat,
That ate the malt
That lay in the house
    that Jack built.

This is the cat,
That killed the rat,
That ate the malt
That lay in the house
    that Jack built.

This is the dog,
That worried the cat,
That killed the rat,
That ate the malt
That lay in the house
    that Jack built.

This is the cow with the crumpled horn,
That tossed the dog,
That worried the cat,
That killed the rat,
That ate the malt
That lay in the house
    that Jack built.

This is the maiden all forlorn,
That milked the cow with the crumpled horn,
That tossed the dog,
That worried the cat,
That killed the rat,
That ate the malt
That lay in the house
    that Jack built.

This is the man all tattered and torn,
That kissed the maiden all forlorn,
That milked the cow with the crumpled horn,
That tossed the dog,
That worried the cat,
That killed the rat,
That ate the malt
That lay in the house
    that Jack built.

This is the priest all shaven and shorn,
That married the man all tattered and torn,
That kissed the maiden all forlorn,
That milked the cow with the crumpled horn,
That tossed the dog,
That worried the cat,
That killed the rat,
That ate the malt
That lay in the house
    that Jack built.

This is the cock that crowed in the morn,
That waked the priest all shaven and shorn,
That married the man all tattered and torn,
That kissed the maiden all forlorn,
That milked the cow with the crumpled horn,
That tossed the dog,
That worried the cat,
That killed the rat,
That ate the malt
That lay in the house
    that Jack built.

This is the farmer sowing his corn,
That kept the cock that crowed in the morn,
That waked the priest all shaven and shorn,
That married the man all tattered and torn,
That kissed the maiden all forlorn,
That milked the cow with the crumpled horn,
That tossed the dog,
That worried the cat,
That killed the rat,
That ate the malt
That lay in the house
   that Jack built.

This is the horse and the hound and the horn,
That belonged to the farmer sowing his corn,
That kept the cock that crowed in the morn,
That waked the priest all shaven and shorn,
That married the man all tattered and torn,
That kissed the maiden all forlorn,
That milked the cow with the crumpled horn,
That tossed the dog,
That worried the cat,
That killed the rat,
That ate the malt
That lay in the house
   that Jack built.

Simple Simon

Simple Simon met a pieman
    Going to the fair;
Says Simple Simon to the pieman,
    Let me taste your ware.

Says the pieman to Simple Simon,
    Show me first your penny;
Says Simple Simon to the pieman,
    Indeed I have not any.

Simple Simon went a-fishing,
    For to catch a whale;
All the water he had got
    Was in his mother's pail.

Simple Simon went a-hunting,
    For to catch a hare;
He rode a goat about the streets,
    But couldn't find one there.

He went to catch a dickey bird,
    And thought he could not fail,
Because he'd got a little salt,
    To put upon its tail.

He went to shoot a wild duck,
    But wild duck flew away;
Says Simon, I can't hit him,
    Because he will not stay.

He went to ride a spotted cow,
    That had a little calf;
She threw him down upon the ground,
    Which made the people laugh.

Once Simon made a great snowball,
    And brought it in to roast;
He laid it down before the fire,
    And soon the ball was lost.

He went to try if cherries ripe
    Did grow upon a thistle;
He pricked his finger very much
    Which made poor Simon whistle.

He went for water in a sieve,
    But soon it ran all through;
And now poor Simple Simon
    Bids you all adieu.

Bedtime

Down with the lambs
Up with the lark,
Run to bed children
Before it gets dark.

Diddle, Diddle, Dumpling

Diddle, diddle, dumpling, my son John,
Went to bed with his trousers on;
One shoe off, and one shoe on,
Diddle, diddle, dumpling, my son John.

Higglety, Pigglety

Higglety, pigglety, pop!
The dog has eaten the mop;
    The pig's in a hurry,
    The cat's in a flurry,
Higglety, pigglety, pop!

The Crows

On the first of March,
The crows begin to search;
By the first of April
They are sitting still;
By the first of May
They've all flown away,
Coming greedy back again
With October's wind and rain.

Caution

Mother, may I go out to swim?
    Yes, my darling daughter.
Hang your clothes on a hickory limb
    And don't go near the water.

A Strange Pig

As I went to Bonner,
    I met a pig
    Without a wig,
Upon my word and honour.

Jack

Jack be nimble,
  Jack be quick,
Jack jump over
  The candlestick.

Bed

Go to bed first,
A golden purse;
Go to bed second,
A golden pheasant;
Go to bed third,
A golden bird.

Three a-Bed

He that lies at the stock,
Shall have a gold rock;
He that lies at the wall,
Shall have a gold ball;
He that lies in the middle,
Shall have a gold fiddle.

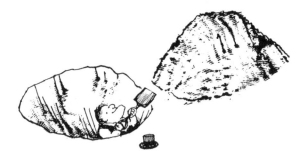

One, Two

1, 2,
Buckle my shoe;

3, 4,
Knock at the door;

5, 6,
Pick up sticks;

7, 8,
Lay them straight;

9, 10,
A big fat hen;

11, 12,
Dig and delve;

13, 14,
Maids a-courting;

15, 16,
Maids in the kitchen;

17, 18,
Maids in waiting;

19, 20,
My plate's empty.

Days in the Month

Thirty days hath September,
April, June, and November;
All the rest have thirty-one,
Excepting February alone,
And that has twenty-eight days clear
And twenty-nine in each leap year.

Star Light

Star light, star bright,
First star I see tonight,
I wish I may, I wish I might,
Have the wish I wish tonight.

Going to St Ives

As I was going to St Ives,
I met a man with seven wives;
Each wife had seven sacks,
Each sack had seven cats,
Each cat had seven kits:
Kits, cats, sacks, and wives,
How many were there going
to St Ives?

(One or None)

Doctor Foster

Doctor Foster went to Gloucester
In a shower of rain;
He stepped in a puddle,
Right up to his middle,
And never went there again.

Punch and Judy

Punch and Judy
   Fought for a pie;
Punch gave Judy
   A knock in the eye.
Says Punch to Judy,
   Will you have any more?
Says Judy to Punch,
   My eye is too sore.

Under a Hill

There was an old woman
   Lived under a hill,
And if she's not gone
   She lives there still.

Tom

Tom, Tom, the piper's son,
Stole a pig and away he run;
   The pig was eat,
   And Tom was beat,
And Tom went howling down the street.

Roses Are Red

Roses are red,
   Violets are blue,
Sugar is sweet
   And so are you.

Tailor of Bicester

The tailor of Bicester,
   He has but one eye;
He cannot cut a pair of green galligaskins,
   If he were to die.

Solomon Grundy

Solomon Grundy,
Born on a Monday,
Christened on Tuesday,
Married on Wednesday,
Took ill on Thursday,
Worse on Friday,
Died on Saturday,
Buried on Sunday.
This is the end
Of Solomon Grundy.

The Fingers

Tom Thumbkin,
Willie Wilkin,
Long Daniel,
Betty Bodkin,
And little Dick.

Pippen Hill

As I was going up Pippen Hill,
    Pippen Hill was dirty.
There I met a pretty miss
    And she dropt me a curtsey.

Little miss, pretty miss,
    Blessings light upon you!
If I had half a crown a day,
    I'd spend it all upon you.

Jackanory

I'll tell you a story
    About Jack a Nory,
And now my story's begun;
    I'll tell you another
    Of Jack and his brother,
And now my story is done.

Kindness

I love little pussy,
    Her coat is so warm,
And if I don't hurt her
    She'll do me no harm.
So I'll not pull her tail,
    Nor drive her away,
But pussy and I
    Very gently will play.
She shall sit by my side,
    And I'll give her some food;
And pussy will love me
    Because I am good.

Jack and Jill and Old Dame Dob

Jack and Jill
Went up the hill,
To fetch a pail of water;
Jack fell down,
And broke his crown,
And Jill came tumbling after.

Then up Jack got,
And home did trot,
As fast as he could caper;
To old Dame Dob,
Who patched his nob
With vinegar and brown paper.

When Jill came in,
How she did grin
To see Jack's paper plaster;
Her mother, vexed,
Did whip her next,
For laughing at Jack's disaster.

Now Jack did laugh
And Jill did cry,
But her tears did soon abate;
Then Jill did say,
That they should play
At see-saw across the gate.

Cock-Crow

The cock's on the wood pile
    Blowing his horn,
The bull's in the barn
    A-threshing the corn,
The maids in the meadow
    Are making the hay,
The ducks in the river
    Are swimming away.

Milking

Cushy cow, bonny, let down thy milk,
And I will give thee a gown of silk;
A gown of silk and a silver tee,
If thou wilt let down thy milk for me.

To the Snail

Snail, snail, put out your horns,
And I'll give you bread and barley corns.

Ring-A-Ring O'Roses

Ring-a-ring o' roses,
A pocket full of posies,
    A-tishoo! A-tishoo!
We all fall down.

The cows are in the meadow
Lying fast asleep,
    A-tishoo! A-tishoo!
We all get up again.
                    Or this way
A ring, a ring o' roses,
A pocket full of posies,
    Ash-a! Ash-a!
All stand still.

The king has sent his daughter
To fetch a pail of water,
    Ash-a! Ash-a!
All bow down.

The bird upon the steeple
Sits high above the people,
    Ash-a! Ash-a!
All kneel down.

The wedding bells are ringing,
The boys and girls are singing,
    Ash-a! Ash-a!
All fall down.

Race Starting

Bell horses, bell horses,
    What time of day?
One o'clock, two o'clock,
    Three and away.

One to make ready,
    And two to prepare;
Good luck to the rider,
    And away goes the mare.

One for the money,
    Two for the show,
Three to make ready,
    And four to go.

The Twelve Days of Christmas

The first day of Christmas
My true love sent to me
A partridge in a pear tree.

The second day of Christmas
My true love sent to me
Two turtle doves, and
A partridge in a pear tree.

The third day of Christmas
My true love sent to me
Three French hens,
Two turtle doves, and
A partridge in a pear tree.

The fourth day of Christmas
My true love sent to me
Four colly birds,
Three French hens,
Two turtle doves, and
A partridge in pear tree.

The fifth day of Christmas
My true love sent to me
Five gold rings,
Four colly birds,
Three French hens,
Two turtle doves, and
A partridge in a pear tree.

The sixth day of Christmas
My true love sent to me
Six geese a-laying,
Five gold rings,
Four colly birds,
Three French hens,
Two turtle doves, and
A partridge in a pear tree.

The seventh day of Christmas
My true love sent to me
Seven swans a-swimming,
Six geese a-laying,
Five gold rings,
Four colly birds,
Three French hens,
Two turtle doves, and
A partridge in a pear tree.

The eighth day of Christmas
My true love sent to me
Eight maids a-milking,
Seven swans a-swimming,
Six geese a-laying,
Five gold rings,
Four colly birds,
Three French hens,
Two turtle doves, and
A partridge in a pear tree.

The ninth day of Christmas
My true love sent to me
Nine drummers drumming,
Eight maids a-milking,
Seven swans a-swimming,
Six geese a-laying,
Five gold rings,
Four colly birds,
Three French hens,
Two turtle doves, and
A partridge in a pear tree.

The tenth day of Christmas
My true love sent to me
Ten pipers piping,
Nine drummers drumming,
Eight maids a-milking,
Seven swans a-swimming,
Six geese a-laying,
Five gold rings,
Four colly birds,
Three French hens,
Two turtle doves, and
A partridge in a pear tree.

The eleventh day of Christmas
My true love sent to me
Eleven ladies dancing,
Ten pipers piping,
Nine drummers drumming,
Eight maids a-milking,
Seven swans a-swimming,
Six geese a-laying,
Five gold rings,
Four colly birds,
Three French hens,
Two turtle doves, and
A partridge in a pear tree.

The twelfth day of Christmas
My true love sent to me
Twelve lords a-leaping,
Eleven ladies dancing,
Ten pipers piping,
Nine drummers drumming,
Eight maids a-milking,
Seven swans a-swimming,
Six geese a-laying,
Five gold rings,
Four colly birds,
Three French hens,
Two turtle doves, and
A partridge in a pear tree.

Cherry Stones

Tinker,

Tailor,

Soldier,

Sailor,

Rich man,

Poor man,

Beggar man,

Thief.

Lady,

Baby,

Gipsy,

Queen.

Jingle Bells

Jingle bells! Jingle bells!
Jingle all the way;
Oh, what fun it is to ride
In a one-horse open sleigh.

Two Pig Stories

This little pig went to market,
This little pig stayed at home,
This little pig had roast beef,
This little pig had none,
And this little pig cried, Wee-wee-
    wee-wee-wee,
All the way home.

This little pig had a rub-a-dub,
This little pig had a scrub-a-scrub,
This little pig-a-wig ran upstairs,
This little pig-a-wig called out, Bears!
Down came the jar with a loud
    Slam! Slam!
And this little pig had all the jam.

Little Bo-Peep

Little Bo-peep has lost her sheep,
  And doesn't know where to find them;
Leave them alone, and they'll come home,
  Bringing their tails behind them.

Little Bo-peep fell fast asleep,
  And dreamt she heard them bleating;
But when she awoke, she found it a joke,
  For they were still a-fleeting.

Then up she took her little crook,
  Determined for to find them;
She found them indeed, but it made her heart bleed,
  For they'd left their tails behind them.

It happened one day, as Bo-peep did stray
  Into a meadow hard by,
Then she espied their tails side by side,
  All hung on a tree to dry.

She heaved a sigh, and wiped her eye,
  And over the hillocks went rambling,
And tried what she could, as a shepherdess should,
  To tack again each to its lambkin.

Bagpipes

Puss came dancing out of a barn
With a pair of bagpipes under her arm;
She could sing nothing but, Fiddle cum fee,
The mouse has married the humble-bee.
Pipe, cat – dance, mouse –
We'll have a wedding at our good house.

The Little Nut Tree

I had a little nut tree,
    Nothing would it bear
But a silver nutmeg
    And a golden pear;
The king of Spain's daughter
    Came to visit me,
And all for the sake
    Of my little nut tree.

The Old Woman

Old woman, old woman,
    Shall we go a-shearing?
Speak a little louder, sir,
    I'm very thick of hearing.
Old woman, old woman,
    Shall I love you dearly?
Thank you very kindly, sir,
    Now I hear you clearly.

Boys and Girls

What are little boys made of, made of?
What are little boys made of?
   Frogs and snails
   And puppy-dogs' tails,
That's what little boys are made of.

What are little girls made of, made of?
What are little girls made of?
   Sugar and spice
   And all things nice,
That's what little girls are made of.

Hush-A-Bye

Hush-a-bye, baby, on the tree top,
When the wind blows the cradle will rock;
When the bough breaks the cradle will fall,
Down will come baby, cradle, and all.

The Death and Burial of Cock Robin

Who killed Cock Robin?
  I, said the Sparrow,
    With my bow and arrow,
I killed Cock Robin.

Who saw him die?
  I, said the Fly,
    With my little eye,
I saw him die.

Who caught his blood?
  I, said the Fish,
    With my little dish,
I caught his blood.

Who'll make his shroud?
  I, said the Beetle,
    With my thread and needle,
I'll make the shroud.

Who'll dig his grave?
  I, said the Owl,
    With my pick and shovel,
I'll dig his grave.

Who'll be the parson?
  I, said the Rook,
    With my little book,
I'll be the parson.

Who'll be the clerk?
  I, said the Lark,
    If it's not in the dark,
I'll be the clerk.

Who'll carry the link?
    I, said the Linnet,
    I'll fetch it in a minute,
I'll carry the link.

Who'll be chief mourner?
    I, said the Dove,
    I mourn for my love,
I'll be chief mourner.

Who'll carry the coffin?
    I, said the Kite,
    If it's not through the night,
I'll carry the coffin.

Who'll bear the pall?
    We, said the Wren,
    Both the cock and the hen,
We'll bear the pall.

Who'll sing a psalm?
    I, said the Thrush,
    As she sat on a bush,
I'll sing a psalm.

Who'll toll the bell?
    I, said the Bull,
    Because I can pull,
So Cock Robin, farewell.

All the birds of the air
    Fell a-sighing and a-sobbing,
    When they heard the bell toll
For poor Cock Robin.

Little Miss Muffet

Little Miss Muffet
Sat on a tuffet,
Eating her curds and whey;
There came a big spider,
Who sat down beside her
And frightened Miss Muffet away.

To the Rain

Rain, rain, go away,
Come again another day,
Little Johnny wants to play.
Rain, rain, go to Spain,
Never show your face again.

Rain

Rain on the green grass,
   And rain on the tree,
Rain on the house-top,
   But not on me.

It's Raining

It's raining, it's pouring,
The old man's snoring;
He got into bed
And bumped his head
And couldn't get up in the
morning.

The Little Boy

Little boy, little boy, where were you born?
Up in the Highlands among the green corn.
Little boy, little boy, where did you sleep?
In the byre with the kye, in the cot with the sheep.

The Three Little Kittens

Three little kittens
They lost their mittens,
   And they began to cry,
Oh, Mother dear,
We sadly fear
   Our mittens we have lost.
What! Lost your mittens,
You naughty kittens!
   Then you shall have no pie.
   Mee-ow, mee-ow, mee-ow.
   No, you shall have no pie.

The three little kittens
Put on their mittens
   And soon ate up the pie;
Oh, Mother dear,
We greatly fear
   Our mittens we have soiled.
What! soiled your mittens,
You naughty kittens!
   Then they began to sigh,
   Mee-ow, mee-ow, mee-ow,
   Then they began to sigh.

The three little kittens
They found their mittens,
   And they began to cry,
Oh, Mother dear,
See here, see here,
   Our mittens we have found.
Put on your mittens,
You silly kittens,
   And you shall have some pie.
   Purr-r, purr-r, purr-r,
   Oh, let us have some pie.

The three little kittens
They washed their mittens,
   And hung them out to dry;
Oh, Mother dear,
Do you not hear,
   Our mittens we have washed.
What! washed your mittens,
Then you're good kittens,
   But I smell a rat close by.
   Mee-ow, mee-ow, mee-ow,
We smell a rat close by.

Ride Away

Ride away, ride away,
  Johnny shall ride,
He shall have a pussy cat
  Tied to one side;
He shall have a little dog
  Tied to the other,
And Johnny shall ride
  To see his grandmother.

The Donkey

Donkey, Donkey, old and grey,
Ope your mouth and gently bray;
Lift your ears and blow your horn,
To wake the world this sleepy morn.

Poll Parrot

Little Poll Parrot
Sat in his garret
Eating toast and tea;
A little brown mouse
Jumped into the house
And stole it all away.

The Flying Pig

Dickery, dickery, dare,
The pig flew up in the air;
The man in brown
Soon brought him down,
Dickery, dickery, dare.

A Ship a-Sailing

I saw a ship a-sailing,
   A-sailing on the sea,
And oh, but it was laden
   With pretty things for thee!

There were comfits in the cabin,
   And apples in the hold;
The sails were made of silk,
   And the masts were all of gold.

The four-and-twenty sailors,
   That stood between the decks,
Were four-and-twenty white mice
   With chains about their necks.

The captain was a duck
   With a packet on his back,
And when the ship began to move
   The captain said, Quack! Quack!

The Wedding

This year,
Next year,
Sometime,
Never.

Coach,
Carriage,
Wheelbarrow,
Dustcart.

Gold,
Silver,
Copper,
Brass.

Silk,
Satin,
Cotton,
Rags.

Big box,
Little box,
Band box,
Bundle.

Boots,
Shoes,
Slippers,
Clogs.

Church,
Chapel,
Cathedral,
Abbey.

Big house,
Little house,
Pig sty,
Barn.

An Old Woman

There was an old woman tossed up in a basket,
Seventeen times as high as the moon;
Where she was going I couldn't but ask it,
For in her hand she carried a broom.

Old woman, old woman, old woman, quoth I,
Where are you going to up so high?
To brush the cobwebs off the sky!
May I go with you? Aye, by-and-by.

Three Ghostesses

Three little ghostesses,
Sitting on postesses,
Eating buttered toastesses,
Greasing their fistesses,
Up to their wristesses.
Oh, what beastesses
To make such feastesses!

Little Nag

I had a little nag
    That trotted up and down;
I bridled him, and saddled him,
    And trotted out of town.

Tweedledum and Tweedledee

Tweedledum and Tweedledee
    Agreed to have a battle,
For Tweedledum said Tweedledee
    Had spoiled his nice new rattle.
Just then flew by a monstrous crow
    As black as a tar-barrel,
Which frightened both the heroes so,
    They quite forgot their quarrel.

If

If all the seas were one sea,
What a *great* sea that would be!
If all the trees were one tree,
What a *great* tree that would be!
And if all the axes were one axe,
What a *great* axe that would be!
And if all the men were one man,
What a *great* man that would be!
And if the *great* man took the *great* axe,
And cut down the *great* tree,
And let it fall into the *great* sea,
What a splish-splash that would be!

Tommy Tucker

Little Tommy Tucker
Sings for his supper:
What shall we give him?
White bread and butter.
How shall he cut it
Without e'er a knife?
How will he be married
Without e'er wife?

Jerry Hall

Jerry Hall,
He is so small,
A rat could eat him,
Hat and all.

Sulky Sue

Here's Sulky Sue;
What shall we do?
Turn her face to the wall
Till she comes to.

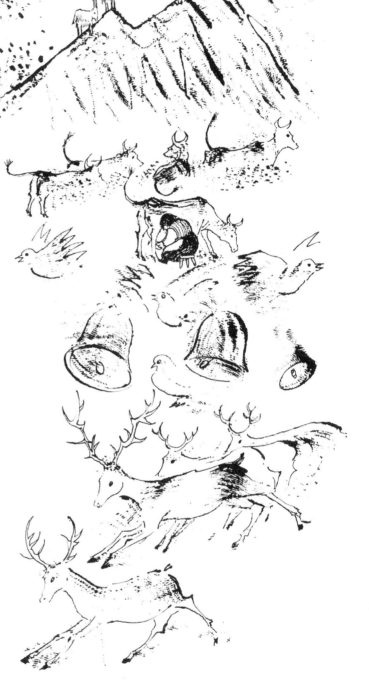

Scottish Lullaby

Hush-a-ba birdie, croon, croon,
Hush-a-ba birdie, croon,
The sheep are gane to the silver wood,
And the cows are gane to the broom, broom.

And it's braw milking the kye, kye,
It's braw milking the kye,
The birds are singing, the bells are ringing,
The wild deer come galloping by, by.

And hush-a-ba birdie, croon, croon,
Hush-a-ba birdie, croon,
The gaits are gane to the mountain hie,
And they'll no be hame till noon, noon.

Encore till the child's asleep.

Tom Thumb's Picture Alphabet

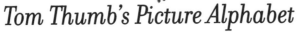

A was an archer,
   who shot at a frog;
B was a butcher,
   and had a great dog.
C was a captain,
   all covered with lace;
D was a drunkard,
   and had a red face.
E was an esquire,
   with pride on his brow.
F was a farmer,
   and followed the plough.
G was a gamester,
   who had but ill-luck;
H was a hunter,
   and hunted a buck.
I was an innkeeper,
   who loved to carouse.
J was a joiner,
   and built up a house.
K was King William,
   once governed this land.
L was a lady,
   who had a white hand.
M was a miser,
   and hoarded up gold;

N was a nobleman,
      gallant and bold.
O was an oyster girl,
      and went about town;
P was a parson,
      and wore a black gown.
Q was a queen,
      who wore a silk slip;
R was a robber,
      and wanted a whip.
S was a sailor,
      and spent all he got;
T was a tinker,
      and mended a pot.
U was a usurer,
      a miserable elf;
V was a vintner,
      who drank all himself.
W was a watchman,
      and guarded the door;
X was expensive,
      and so became poor.
Y was a youth,
      that did not love school;
Z was a zany,
      a poor harmless fool.

Riddles

The land was white,
    The seed was black;
It will take a good scholar
    To riddle me that.

Little Billy Breek
Sits by the reek,
He has more horns
Than all the king's sheep.

I have a little sister, they call her Peep-Peep,
She wades the waters deep, deep, deep;
She climbs the mountains high, high, high;
Poor little creature she has but one eye.

Higher than a house,
Higher than a tree;
Oh, whatever can that be?

A Walnut

As soft as silk, as white as milk,
As bitter as gall, a strong wall,
And a green coat covers me all.

THE EAGLE
Licenced to sell Beer, Ale, Wine, Spirits, Tobacco

Pop Goes the Weasel

Up and down the City Road,
In and out the Eagle,
That's the way the money goes,
Pop goes the weasel!

Half a pound of tuppenny rice,
Half a pound of treacle,
Mix it up and make it nice,
Pop goes the weasel!

Every night when I go out
The monkey's on the table;
Take a stick and knock it off,
Pop goes the weasel!

My Mother Said

My mother said, I never should
Play with the gypsies in the wood.
If I did, then she would say:
Naughty girl to disobey.
Your hair shan't curl and your shoes shan't shine,
You gypsy girl you shan't be mine,
And my father said that if I did,
He'd rap my head with the teapot lid.
My mother said that I never should
Play with the gypsies in the wood.
The wood was dark, the grass was green;
By came Sally with a tambourine.
I went to sea — no ship to get across;
I paid ten shillings for a blind white horse.
I upped on his back and was off in a crack,
Sally tell my mother I shall never come back.

The Mulberry Bush

Here we go round the mulberry bush,
The mulberry bush, the mulberry bush,
Here we go round the mulberry bush,
On a cold and frosty morning.

This is the way we wash our hands,
Wash our hands, wash our hands,
This is the way we wash our hands,
On a cold and frosty morning.

This is the way we wash our clothes,
Wash our clothes, wash our clothes.
This is the way we wash our clothes,
On a cold and frosty morning.

This is the way we go to school,
Go to school, go to school,
This is the way we go to school,
On a cold and frosty morning.

This is the way we come out of school,
Come out of school, come out of school,
This is the way we come out of school,
On a cold and frosty morning.

Winter

Cold and raw the north wind
    doth blow,
Bleak in the morning early;
All the hills are covered with
    snow,
And winter's now come fairly.

Georgie Porgie

Georgie Porgie, pudding and pie,
Kissed the girls and made them cry;
When the boys came out to play,
Georgie Porgie ran away.

The Little Girl

There was a little girl, and she had a little curl
  Right in the middle of her forehead;
When she was good she was very, very good,
  But when she was bad she was horrid.

Jack Horner

Little Jack Horner
Sat in the corner,
Eating his Christmas pie;
He put in his thumb,
And pulled out a plum,
And said, What a good boy am I!

Contrary Mary

Mary, Mary, quite contrary,
    How does your garden grow?
With silver bells and cockle shells,
    And pretty maids all in a row.

The Cat and the Fiddle

Hey diddle, diddle,
  The cat and the fiddle,
The cow jumped over the moon;
  The little dog laughed
  To see such sport,
And the dish ran away with
  the spoon.

The Little Black Dog

The little black dog ran round the house,
And set the bull a-roaring,
And drove the monkey in the boat,
Who set the oars a-rowing,
And scared the cock upon the rock,
Who cracked his throat with crowing.

Jemmy Dawson

Brave news is come to town,
    Brave news is carried;
Brave news is come to town,
    Jemmy Dawson's married.

First he got a porridge-pot,
    Then he bought a ladle;
Then he got a wife and child,
    And then he bought a cradle.

Churning

Come, butter, come,
Come, butter, come;
Peter stands at the gate
Waiting for a butter cake.
Come, butter, come.

Two Birds

There were two birds sat on a stone,
    Fa, la, la, la, lal, de;
One flew away, and then there was one,
    Fa, la, la, la, lal, de;
The other flew after, and then there was none,
    Fa, la, la, la, lal, de;
And so the poor stone was left all alone,
    Fa, la, la, la, lal, de.

What Can the Matter Be?

O dear, what can the matter be?
Dear, dear, what can the matter be?
O dear, what can the matter be?
Johnny's so long at the fair.

He promised he'd buy me a fairing
    should please me
And then for a kiss, oh! he vowed
    he would tease me,
He promised he'd buy me a bunch of blue ribbons
To tie up my bonny brown hair.

And it's O dear, what can the matter be?
Dear, dear, what can the matter be?
O dear, what can the matter be?
Johnny's so long at the fair.

He promised to buy me a pair of sleeve buttons,
A pair of new garters that cost him but two pence,
He promised he'd bring me a bunch of blue ribbons
To tie up my bonny brown hair.

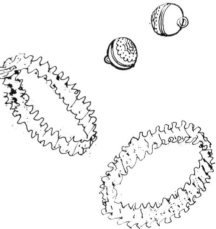

And it's O dear, what can the matter be?
Dear, dear, what can the matter be?
O dear, what can the matter be?
Johnny's so long at the fair.

He promised he'd buy me a basket of posies,
A garland of lilies, a garland of roses,
A little straw hat, to set off the blue ribbons,
That tie up my bonny brown hair.

The Fox's Foray

A fox jumped up one winter's night,
And begged the moon to give him light,
For he'd many miles to trot that night
Before he reached his den O!
    Den O! Den O!
For he'd many miles to trot that night
Before he reached his den O!

The first place he came to was a farmer's yard,
Where the ducks and the geese declared it hard
That their nerves should be shaken and their rest so marred
By a visit from Mr Fox O!
    Fox O! Fox O!
That their nerves should be shaken and their rest so marred
By a visit from Mr Fox O!

He took the grey goose by the neck,
And swung him right across his back;
The grey goose cried out, Quack, quack, quack,
With his legs hanging dangling down O!
    Down O! Down O!
The grey goose cried out, Quack, quack, quack,
With his legs hanging dangling down O!

Old Mother Slipper Slopper jumped out of bed,
And out of the window she popped her head:
Oh! John, John, John, the grey goose is gone,
And the fox is off to his den O!
    Den O! Den O!
Oh! John, John, John, the grey goose is gone,
And the fox is off to his den O!

John ran up to the top of the hill,
And blew his whistle loud and shrill;
Said the fox, That is very pretty music; still —
I'd rather be in my den O!
    Den O! Den O!
Said the fox, That is very pretty music; still —
I'd rather be in my den O!

The fox went back to his hungry den,
And his dear little foxes, eight, nine, ten;
Quoth they, Good daddy, you must go there again,
If you bring such good cheer from the farm O!
    Farm O! Farm O!
Quoth they, Good daddy, you must go there again,
If you bring such good cheer from the farm O!

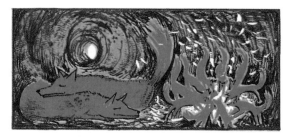

The fox and his wife, without any strife,
Said they never ate a better goose in all their life:
They did very well without fork or knife,
And the little ones picked the bones O!
    Bones O! Bones O!
They did very well without fork or knife,
And the little ones picked the bones O!

The Owl

Of all the gay birds that e'er I did see,
The owl is the fairest by far to me,
For all day long she sits in a tree,
And when the night comes away flies she.

The Moon

I see the moon,
    And the moon sees me;
God bless the moon,
    And God bless me.

Mister Rusticap

As I went over Lincoln Bridge,
I met Mister Rusticap;
Pins and needles on his back,
A-going to Thorney fair.

Blow, Wind, Blow

Blow, wind, blow!
And go, mill, go!
That the miller may grind his corn;
That the baker may take it,
And into bread make it,
And bring us a loaf in the morn.

A Man in the Wilderness

A man in the wilderness asked me,
How many strawberries grow in the sea.
I answered him, as I thought good,
As many red herrings as swim in the wood.

The Mocking Bird

Hush, little baby, don't say a word,
Papa's going to buy you a mocking bird.

If the mocking bird won't sing,
Papa's going to buy you a diamond ring.

If the diamond ring turns to brass,
Papa's going to buy you a looking-glass.

If the looking-glass gets broke,
Papa's going to buy you a billy-goat.

If that billy goat runs away,
Papa's going to buy you another today.

Six Little Mice

Six little mice sat down to spin;
Pussy passed by and she peeped in.
What are you doing, my little men?
Weaving coats for gentlemen.
Shall I come in and cut off your threads?
No, no, Mistress Pussy, you'd bite off
    our heads
Oh, no, I'll not; I'll help you to spin.
That may be so, but you don't come in.

The Apple Tree

As I went up the apple tree
All the apples fell on me;
Bake a pudding, bake a pie,
Send it up to John MacKay;
John MacKay is not in,
Send it up to the man in the moon.

Missing Commas II

I saw a fishpond all on fire
I saw a house bow to a squire
I saw a parson twelve feet high
I saw a cottage near the sky
I saw a balloon made of lead
I saw a coffin drop down dead
I saw two sparrows run a race
I saw two horses making lace
I saw a girl just like a cat
I saw a kitten wear a hat
I saw a man who saw these too
And said though strange
    they all were true.

Counting Rhymes

One-ery, two-ery, tickery, seven,
Hallibo, crackibo, ten and eleven,
Spin, span, muskidan,
Twiddle-um, twaddle-um, twenty-one.

One-ery, two-ery, ickery, Ann,
Phillisy, phollisy, Nicholas John,
Quever, quaver, Irish Mary,
Stickerum, stackerum, buck.

Fishes

Little fishes in a brook,
Father caught them on a hook,
Mother fried them in a pan,
Johnnie eats them like a man.

Apples

Here's to thee, old apple tree,
Whence thou may'st bud
And whence thou may'st blow,
And whence thou may'st bear apples
    enow;
Hats full and caps full,
Bushels full and sacks full,
And our pockets full too.

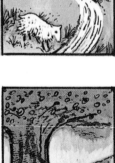

Where I Went

I went up the high hill,
There I saw a climbing goat;
I went down by the running rill,
There I saw a ragged sheep;
I went out to the roaring sea,
There I saw a tossing boat;
I went under the green tree,
There I saw two doves asleep.

Three Blind Mice

Three blind mice, see how they run!
They all ran after the farmer's wife,
Who cut off their tails with a carving knife,
Did you ever see such a thing in your life,
    As three blind mice?

Daffy-Down-Dilly

Daffy-down-dilly is new come to town,
With a yellow petticoat, and a green gown.

Blind Man's Buff

Blind man, blind man,
　Sure you can't see?
Turn round three times,
　And try to catch me.
Turn east, turn west,
　Catch as you can,
Did you think you'd caught me?
　Blind, blind man!

This is the Way the Ladies Ride

This is the way the ladies ride,
　Nim, nim, nim, nim,
This is the way the gentlemen ride,
　Trim, trim, trim, trim.
This is the way the farmers ride,
　Trot, trot, trot, trot.
This is the way the huntsmen ride,
　A-gallop, a-gallop, a-gallop, a-gallop.
This is the way the ploughboys ride,
　Hobble-dy-gee, hobble-dy-gee.

The Squirrel

The winds they did blow,
   The leaves they did wag;
Along came a beggar boy,
   And put me in his bag.

He took me up to London,
   A lady did me buy,
Put me in a silver cage,
   And hung me up on high.

With apples by the fire,
   And nuts for to crack,
Besides a little feather bed
   To rest my little back.

If Wishes Were Horses

If wishes were horses, beggars would ride.
If turnips were watches, I would
   wear one by my side.
And if "ifs" and "ands"
Were pots and pans,
There'd be no work for tinkers!

The Soldier and the Maid

Oh, soldier, soldier, will you marry me,
   With your musket, fife, and drum?
Oh no, pretty maid, I cannot marry you,
   For I have no coat to put on.

Then away she went to the tailor's shop
   As fast as legs could run,
And bought him one of the very very best,
   And the soldier put it on.

Oh, soldier, soldier, will you marry me,
   With your musket, fife, and drum?
Oh no, pretty maid, I cannot marry you,
   For I have no shoes to put on.

Then away she went to the cobbler's shop
   As fast as legs could run,
And bought him a pair of the very very best,
   And the soldier put them on.

Oh, soldier, soldier, will you marry me,
   With your musket, fife, and drum?
Oh no, pretty maid, I cannot marry you,
   For I have no socks to put on.

Then away she went to the sock-maker's shop
   As fast as legs could run,
And bought him a pair of the very very best,
   And the soldier put them on.

Oh, soldier, soldier, will you marry me,
   With your musket, fife, and drum?
Oh no, pretty maid, I cannot marry you,
   For I have no hat to put on.

Then away she went to the hatter's shop
   As fast as legs could run,
And bought him one of the very very best,
   And the soldier put it on.

Oh, soldier, soldier, will you marry me,
   With your musket, fife, and drum?
Oh no, pretty maid, I cannot marry you,
   For I have a wife at home.

If All the World

If all the world was paper,
And all the sea was ink,
If all the trees were bread and cheese,
What should we have to drink?

Sally

Sally go round the sun,
Sally go round the moon,
Sally go round the chimney-pots
On a Saturday afternoon.

Robin the Bobbin

Robin the Bobbin,
    the big-bellied Ben,
He ate more meat
    than fourscore men;
He ate a cow,
    he ate a calf,
He ate a butcher
    and a half,
He ate a church,
    he ate a steeple,
He ate a priest
    and all the people!
A cow and a calf,
An ox and a half,
A church and a steeple,
And all the good people,
And yet he complained
    that his stomach wasn't full.

Tommy Tittlemouse

Little Tommy Tittlemouse
Lived in a little house;
He caught fishes
In other men's ditches.

What's the News?

What's the news of the day?
Good neighbour, I pray?
They say the balloon
Is gone up to the moon.

The Sky

Red sky at night,
Shepherd's delight;
Red sky in the morning,
Shepherd's warning.

Two Robins

A robin and a robin's son
Once went to town to buy a bun.
They couldn't decide on plum or plain,
And so they went back home again.

Going to Bed

Go to bed late,
Stay very small;
Go to bed early,
Grow very tall.

A Prayer

Now I lay me down to sleep,
I pray the Lord my soul to keep;
And if I die before I wake,
I pray the Lord my soul to take.

Pussy Cat

Pussy cat ate the dumplings,
Pussy cat ate the dumplings,
   Mamma stood by,
    And cried, Oh, fie!
Why did you eat the dumplings?

The Old Woman in a Shoe

There was an old woman who lived in a shoe,
She had so many children she didn't know what to do;
She gave them some broth without any bread;
She whipped them all soundly and put them to bed.

Peter

Peter, Peter, pumpkin eater,
Had a wife and couldn't keep her;
He put her in a pumpkin shell
And there he kept her very well.

Three Young Rats

Three young rats with black felt hats,
Three young ducks with white straw flats,
Three young dogs with curling tails,
Three young cats with demi-veils,
Went out to walk with three young pigs
In satin vests and sorrel wigs;
But suddenly it chanced to rain
And so they all went home again.

Jeremiah

Jeremiah, blow the fire,
    Puff, puff, puff!
First you blow it gently,
    Then you blow it rough.

Babylon

How many miles to Babylon?
Three-score and ten.
Can I get there by candle-light?
Yes, and back again.
If your heels are nimble and light,
You may get there by candle-light.

Daddy

Bring Daddy home
   With a fiddle and a drum,
A pocket full of spices,
   An apple and a plum.

The Coachman

Up at Piccadilly oh!
   The coachman takes his stand,
And when he meets a pretty girl,
   He takes her by the hand;
     Whip away for ever oh!
     Drive away so clever oh!
     All the way to Bristol oh!
He drives her four-in-hand.

Barber, Barber

Barber, barber, shave a pig,
How many hairs will make a wig?
Four and twenty, that's enough.
Give the barber a pinch of snuff.

Christmas is Coming

Christmas is coming,
    The geese are getting fat,
Please to put a penny
    In the old man's hat.
If you haven't got a penny,
    A ha'penny will do;
If you haven't got a ha'penny,
    Then God bless you!

Good Friday

Hot cross buns, hot cross buns;
One a penny poker,
Two a penny tongs,
Three a penny fire shovel,
Hot cross buns.

Humpty Dumpty

Humpty Dumpty sat on a wall,
Humpty Dumpty had a great fall;
All the King's horses and all the King's men
Couldn't put Humpty together again.

Polly

Polly put the kettle on,
Polly put the kettle on,
Polly put the kettle on,
   We'll all have tea.

Sukey take it off again,
Sukey take it off again,
Sukey take if off again,
   They've all gone away.

Or

Polly put the kettle on,
Sally blow the bellows strong,
Molly call the muffin man,
   We'll all have tea.

The Love-Sick Frog

A frog he would a-wooing go,
  Heigh ho! says Rowley,
Whether his mother would let him or no.
  With a rowley, powley, gammon and spinach,
  Heigh ho! says Anthony Rowley.

So off he set with his opera hat,
  Heigh ho! says Rowley,
And on the road he met with a rat.
  With a rowley, powley, gammon and spinach,
  Heigh ho! says Anthony Rowley.

Pray, Mister Rat, will you go with me?
  Heigh ho! says Rowley,
Kind Mistress Mousey for to see?
  With a rowley, powley, gammon and spinach,
  Heigh ho! says Anthony Rowley.

They came to the door of Mousey's hall,
  Heigh ho! says Rowley,
They gave a loud knock, and they gave a loud call.
  With a rowley, powley, gammon and spinach,
  Heigh ho! says Anthony Rowley.

Pray, Mistress Mouse, are you within?
  Heigh ho! says Rowley,
Oh yes, kind sirs, I'm sitting to spin.
  With a rowley, powley, gammon and spinach,
  Heigh ho! says Anthony Rowley.

Pray, Mistress Mouse, will you give us some beer?
  Heigh ho! says Rowley,
For Froggy and I are fond of good cheer.
  With a rowley, powley, gammon and spinach,
  Heigh ho! says Anthony Rowley.

Pray, Master Frog, will you give us a song?
    Heigh ho! says Rowley,
Let it be something that's not very long.
    With a rowley, powley, gammon and spinach,
    Heigh ho! says Anthony Rowley.

Indeed, Mistress Mouse, replied Mister Frog,
    Heigh ho! says Rowley,
A cold has made me as hoarse as a dog.
    With a rowley, powley, gammon and spinach,
    Heigh ho! says Anthony Rowley.

Since you have a cold, Mister Frog, Mousey said,
    Heigh ho! says Rowley,
I'll sing you a song that I have just made.
    With a rowley, powley, gammon and spinach,
    Heigh ho! says Anthony Rowley.

But while they were all a-merry-making,
    Heigh ho! says Rowley,
A cat and her kittens came tumbling in.
    With a rowley, powley, gammon and spinach,
    Heigh ho! says Anthony Rowley.

The cat she seized the rat by the crown,
    Heigh ho! says Rowley,
The kittens they pulled the little mouse down.
    With a rowley, powley, gammon and spinach,
    Heigh ho! says Anthony Rowley.

This put Mister Frog in a terrible fright,
    Heigh ho! says Rowley,
He took up his hat and he wished them good-night.
    With a rowley, powley, gammon and spinach,
    Heigh ho! says Anthony Rowley.

But as Froggy was crossing over a brook,
    Heigh ho! says Rowley,
A lily-white duck came and gobbled him up.
    With a rowley, powley, gammon and spinach,
    Heigh ho! says Anthony Rowley.

The Wise Men of Gotham

Three wise men of Gotham
Went to sea in a bowl
If the bowl had been stronger,
My story would have been longer.

Pussy Cat

Pussy cat, pussy cat,
Where have you been?
I've been to London
To look at the Queen.
Pussy cat, pussy cat,
What did you there?
I frightened a little mouse
Under her chair.

To the Ladybird

Ladybird, ladybird,
    Fly away home,
Your house is on fire
    And your children all gone;
All except one
    And that's little Ann
And she has crept under
    The warming pan.

Hay Making

Willy boy, Willy boy, where are you going?
I will go with you if that I may.
I'm going to the meadow to see them a-mowing,
I am going to help them to make the new hay.

Little Girl

Little girl, little girl,
    Where have you been?
I've been to see grandmother
    Over the green.
What did she give you?
    Milk in a can.
What did you say for it?
    Thank you, Grandam.

Bow-Wow

Bow-wow, says the dog,
Mew, mew, says the cat,
Grunt, grunt, goes the hog,
And squeak goes the rat.
Tu-whu, says the owl,
Caw, caw, says the crow,
Quack, quack, says the duck,
And what cuckoos say you know.

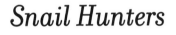

Snail Hunters

Four and twenty tailors
   Went to kill a snail,
The best man amongst them
   Durst not touch her tail;
She put our her horns
   Like a little Kyloe cow,
Run, tailors, run,
   Or she'll kill you all e'en now.

The Owl

A wise old owl sat in an oak,
The more he heard the less he spoke;
The less he spoke the more he heard.
Why aren't we all like that wise old bird?

Pease Porridge

Pease porridge hot,
Pease porridge cold,
Pease porridge in the pot
Nine says old.
Some like it hot,
Some like it cold,
Some like it in the pot
Nine days old.

Ding, Dong, Bell

Ding, dong, bell,
Pussy's in the well.
Who put her in?
Little Johnny Green.
Who pulled her out?
Little Tommy Stout.
What a naughty boy was that
To try to drown poor pussy cat,
Who never did him any harm,
And killed the mice in his father's barn.

Mary's Lamb

Mary had a little lamb,
　Its fleece was white as snow;
And everywhere that Mary went
　The lamb was sure to go.
It followed her to school one day,
　That was against the rule;
It made the children laugh and play
　To see a lamb at school.

And so the teacher turned it out,
　But still it lingered near,
And waited patiently about
　Till Mary did appear.
Why does the lamb love Mary so?
　The eager children cry;
Why, Mary loves the lamb, you know,
　The teacher did reply.

To the Magpie

Magpie, magpie, flutter and flee,
Turn up your tail and good luck
　　come to me.
One for sorrow, two for joy,
Three for a girl, four for a boy,
Five for silver, six for gold,
Seven for a secret ne'er to be told.

My Black Hen

Hickety, pickety, my black hen,
She lays eggs for gentlemen;
Gentlemen come every day
To see what my black hen doth lay.

Banbury Fair

As I was going to Banbury,
Upon a summer's day,
My dame had butter, eggs, and fruit,
And I had corn and hay.
Joe drove the ox, and Tom the swine,
Dick took the foal and mare;
I sold them all — then home to dine,
From famous Banbury fair.

The Queen of Hearts

The Queen of Hearts
She made some tarts,
All on a summer's day;
The Knave of Hearts
He stole those tarts,
And took them clean away.

The King of Hearts
Called for the tarts,
And beat the knave full sore;
The Knave of Hearts
Brought back the tarts,
And vowed he'd steal no more.

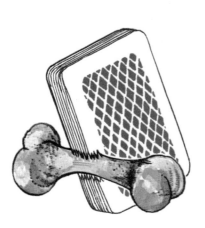

Missing Commas III

I saw a pack of cards gnawing a bone
I saw a dog seated on Britain's throne
I saw a Queen shut up within a box
I saw a shilling driving a fat ox
I saw a man lying in a muff all night
I saw a glove reading news by candle-light
I saw a woman not a twelvemonth old
I saw a greatcoat all of solid gold
I saw two buttons telling of their dreams
I heard my friends, who wish'd I'd quit these themes.

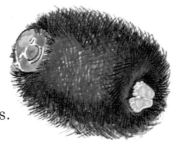

Tickly, Tickly

Tickly, tickly, on your knee,
If you laugh you don't love me.

Sing, Sing

Sing, sing,
  What shall I sing?
The cat's run away
  With the pudding string!

Do, do,
  What shall I do?
That cat's run away
  With the pudding too!

The Wind

My lady Wind, my lady Wind,
Went round the house to find
  A chink to set her foot in;
She tried the key-hole in the door,
She tried the crevice in the floor,
  And drove the chimney soot in.

Cock a Doodle Doo

Cock a doodle doo!
My dame has lost her shoe,
My master's lost his fiddling stick
And knows not what to do.

Cock a doodle doo!
What is my dame to do?
Till master finds his fiddling stick
She'll dance without her shoe.

Cock a doodle doo!
My dame has found her shoe,
And master's found his fiddling stick,
Sing doodle doodle doo.

Cock a doodle doo!
My dame will dance with you,
While master fiddles his fiddling stick
For dame and doodle doo.

London Bridge

London Bridge is broken down,
 Broken down, broken down,
London Bridge is broken down,
 My fair lady.

Build it up with wood and clay,
 Wood and clay, wood and clay,
Build it up with wood and clay,
 My fair lady.

Wood and clay will wash away,
 Wash away, wash away,
Wood and clay will wash away,
 My fair lady.

Build it up with bricks and mortar,
 Bricks and mortar, bricks and mortar,
Build it up with bricks and mortar,
 My fair lady.

Bricks and mortar will not stay,
 Will not stay, will not stay,
Bricks and mortar will not stay,
 My fair lady.

Build it up with iron and steel,
 Iron and steel, iron and steel,
Build it up with iron and steel,
 My fair lady.

Iron and steel will bend and bow,
 Bend and bow, bend and bow,
Iron and steel will bend and bow,
 My fair lady.

Build it up with silver and gold,
 Silver and gold, silver and gold,
Build it up with silver and gold,
 My fair lady.

Silver and gold will be stolen away,
 Stolen away, stolen away,
Silver and gold will be stolen away,
 My fair lady.

Set a man to watch all night,
 Watch all night, watch all night,
Set a man to watch all night,
 My fair lady.

Suppose the man should fall asleep,
 Fall asleep, fall asleep,
Suppose the man should fall asleep,
 My fair lady.

Give him a pipe to smoke all night,
 Smoke all night, smoke all night,
Give him a pipe to smoke all night,
 My fair lady.

The Mischievous Raven

A farmer went trotting upon his grey mare,
 Bumpety, bumpety, bump!
With his daughter behind him so rosy and fair,
 Lumpety, lumpety, lump!

A raven cried, Croak! and they all tumbled down,
 Bumpety, bumpety, bump!
The mare broke her knees and the farmer his crown,
 Lumpety, lumpety, lump!

The mischievous raven flew laughing away,
 Bumpety, bumpety, bump!
And vowed he would serve them the same the next day,
 Lumpety, lumpety, lump!

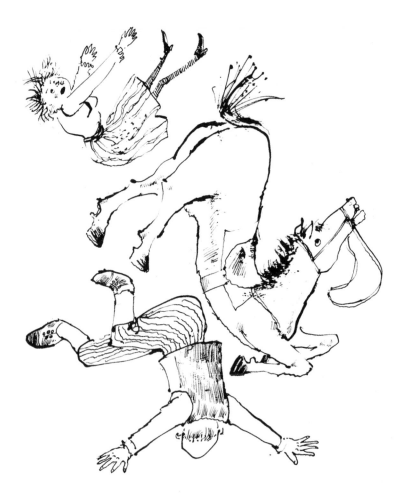

Dance to Your Daddy

Dance to your daddy,
   My little babby,
Dance to your daddy,
   My little lamb.

You shall have a fishy
   In a little dishy
You shall have a fishy
   When the boat comes in.

You shall have an apple,
   You shall have a plum,
You shall have a rattle-basket
   When your daddy comes home.

Boys and Girls Come Out to Play

Boys and girls come out to play,
The moon doth shine as bright as day.
Leave your supper and leave your sleep,
And join your playfellows in the street.
Come with a whoop and come with a call,
Come with a good will or not at all.
Up the ladder and down the wall,
A half-penny loaf will serve us all;
You find milk, and I'll find flour,
And we'll have a pudding in half an hour.

Down by the River

Down by the river
   Where the green grass grows
Pretty Polly Perkins
   Bleaches her clothes.
She laughs and she sings,
   And she sings so sweet.
She calls, Come over,
   Across the street.
He kissed her, he kissed her,
   He took her to the town;
He bought her a ring
   And a damascene gown.

A Cottage in Fife

   In a cottage in Fife
   Lived a man and his wife,
Who, believe me, were comical folk:
   For, to people's surprise,
   They both saw with their eyes,
And their tongues moved whenever they spoke.
   When quite fast asleep,
   I've been told that to keep
Their eyes open they could not contrive;
   They walked on their feet,
   And 'twas thought what they eat
Helped, with drinking, to keep them alive.

Yankee Doodle

Yankee Doodle came to town,
   Riding on a pony;
He stuck a feather in his cap
   And called it macaroni.

Green Grass

A dis, a dis, a green grass,
　　A dis, a dis, a dis;
Come all you pretty fair maids
　　And dance along with us.

For we are going a-roving,
　　A-roving in this land;
We'll take this pretty fair maid,
　　We'll take her by the hand.

You shall have a duck, my dear,
　　And you shall have a drake;
And you shall have a young prince,
　　A young prince for your sake.

And if this young prince chance to die,
　　You shall have another;
The bells will ring, and the birds will sing,
　　And we'll all clap hands together.

Jolly Miller

There was a jolly miller once,
　　Lived on the river Dee;
He worked and sang from morn till
　　　　night,
　　No lark more blithe than he.
And this the burden of his song
　　Forever used to be,
I care for nobody, no! not I,
　　If nobody cares for me.

A Nail

For want of a nail
The shoe was lost,
For want of a shoe
The horse was lost,
For want of a horse
The rider was lost,
For want of a rider
The battle was lost,
For want of a battle
The kingdom was lost,
And all for the want
Of a horse shoe nail.

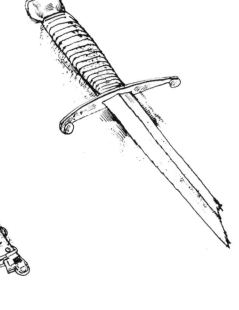

Dame Trot

Dame Trot and her cat
Sat down for a chat;
The Dame sat on this side
And puss sat on that.

Puss, says the Dame,
Can you catch a rat,
Or a mouse in the dark?
Purr, says the cat.

The Key of the Kingdom

This is the key of the kingdom:
In that kingdom is a city,
In that city is a town,
In that town there is a street,
In that street there winds a lane,
In that lane there is a yard,
In that yard there is a house,
In that house there waits a room,
In that room there is a bed,
On that bed there is a basket,
   A basket of flowers.

Flowers in the basket,
Basket on the bed,
Bed in the chamber,
Chamber in the house,
House in the weedy yard,
Yard in the winding lane,
Lane in the broad street,
Street in the high town,
Town in the city,
City in the kingdom:
   This is the key of the kingdom.

Lucy and Kitty

Lucky Locket lost her pocket,
   Kitty Fisher found it;
Not a penny was there in it,
   Only ribbon round it.

Rabbit Skin

Bye, baby bunting,
Daddy's gone a-hunting,
Gone to get a rabbit skin
To wrap the baby bunting in.

Five Hens

There was an old man who lived in Middle Row,
He had five hens and a name for them, oh!
  Bill and Ned and Battock,
  Cut-her-foot and Pattock,
  Chuck, my lady Pattock,
  Go to thy nest and lay.

Moses

Moses supposes his toeses are roses,
But Moses supposes erroneously;
For nobody's toeses are posies of roses
As Moses supposes his toeses to be.

Gunpowder Plot Day

Please to remember
The Fifth of November,
Gunpowder treason and plot;
I see no reason
Why gunpowder treason
Should ever be forgot.

Oh, That I Were

Oh, that I were
    Where I would be,
Then would I be,
    Where I am not;
But where I am
    There I must be,
And where I would be
    I can not.

Peter Piper

Peter Piper picked a peck of pickled pepper;
A peck of pickled pepper Peter Piper picked.
If Peter Piper picked a peck of pickled pepper,
Where's the peck of pickled pepper
    Peter Piper picked?

A, Apple Pie

A was an
apple pie

B
Bit it

C
Cut it

D
Dealt it

E
Eat it

F
Fought for it

G
Got it

H
Had it

I
Inspected it

J
Joined for it

K
Kept it

L
Longed for it

M
Mourned for it

N
Nodded at it

O
Opened it

P
Peeped in it

Q
Quartered it

R
Ran for it

S
Stole it

T
Took it

U
Upset it

V
Viewed it

W
Wanted it

XYZ and &
All wished for
a piece in hand.

Oranges and Lemons

Gay go up and Gay go down,
To ring the bells of London Town.

Bull's eyes and targets,
Say the bells of St. Marg'ret's.

Brickbats and tiles,
Say the bells of St. Giles'.

Oranges and lemons,
Say the bells of St. Clement's.

Pancakes and fritters,
Say the bells of St. Peter's.

Two sticks and an apple,
Say the bells at Whitechapel.

Old Father Baldpate,
Say the slow bells at Aldgate.

Maids in white aprons,
Say the bells at St. Catherine's.

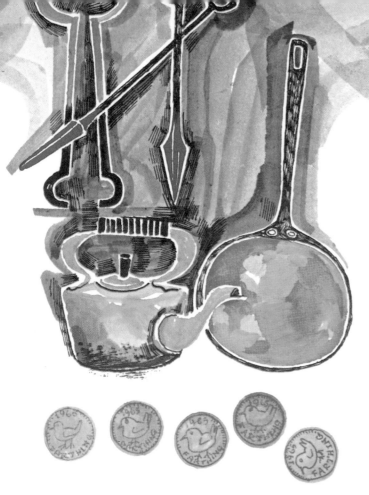

Pokers and tongs,
Say the bells at St. John's.

Kettles and pans,
Say the bells at St. Anne's.

You owe me five farthings,
Say the bells of St. Martin's.

When will you pay me?
Say the bells at Old Bailey.

When I go rich.
Say the bells at Shoreditch.

Pray, when will that be?
Say the bells at Stepney.

I'm sure I don't know,
Says the great bell at Bow.

Here comes a candle to light you to bed,
Here comes a chopper
to chop off your head.

Ride a Cock-Horse

Ride a cock-horse to Banbury Cross,
To see a fine lady upon a white horse;
Rings on her fingers and bells on her toes,
And she shall have music wherever she goes.

My Maid Mary

My maid Mary,
    She minds the dairy,
While I go a-hoeing and mowing each morn;
    Merrily run the reel,
    And the little spinning wheel,
Whilst I am singing and mowing my corn.

The Lion and the Unicorn

The lion and the unicorn
    Were fighting for the crown;
The lion beat the unicorn
    All around the town.

Some gave them white bread,
    And some gave them brown;
Some gave them plum cake
    And drummed them out of town.

Tom Tinker's Dog

Bow, wow, wow,
Whose dog art thou?
Little Tom Tinker's dog,
Bow, wow, wow.

Willie Winkie

Wee Willie Winkie runs through the town,
Upstairs and downstairs in his night-gown,
Rapping at the window, crying through the lock,
Are the children all in bed, for now it's eight o' clock?

Hoddley, Poddley

Hoddley, poddley, puddle and fogs,
Cats are to marry the poodle dogs;
Cats in blue jackets and dogs in red hats,
What will become of the mice and the rats?

Rock-a-Bye

Rock-a-bye, baby,
   Thy cradle is green,
Father's a nobleman,
   Mother's a queen;
And Betty's a lady,
   And wears a gold ring;
And Johnny's a drummer,
   And drums for the king.

Jack-a-Dandy

Naughty Pauty Jack-a-Dandy
Stole a piece of sugar candy
From the grocer's shoppy-shop,
And away did hoppy-hop.

Riddles

Clothed in yellow, red and green,
I prate before the king and queen;
Of neither house nor land possessed,
By lords and knights I am caressed.

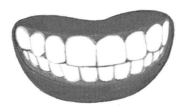

Thirty white horses
Upon a red hill,
Now they stamp,
Now they champ,
Now they stand still.

Highty tighty, paradighty,
Clothed all in green,
The king could not read it,
No more could the queen;
They sent for the wise men
From out of the East,
Who said it had horns,
But was not a beast.

Spring

March winds and April showers
Bring forth May flowers.

The Wind

When the wind is in the east,
'Tis neither good for man nor beast;
When the wind is in the north,
The skilful fisher goes not forth;
When the wind is in the south,
It blows the bait in the fishes' mouth;
When the wind is in the west,
Then 'tis at the very best.

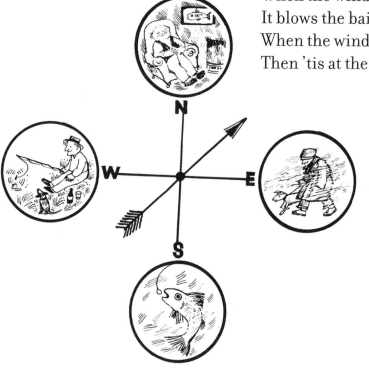

The Riot

The sow came in with the saddle,
The little pig rocked the cradle,
The dish jumped up on the table
To see the pot swallow the ladle.
The spit that stood behind the door
Threw the pudding-stick on the floor.
   Odd's-bobs! says the gridiron,
     Can't you agree?
  I'm the head constable,
     Bring them to me.

Great A

Great A, little a,
   Bouncing B,
The cat's in the cupboard
   And can't see me.

Cobbler, Cobbler

Cobbler, cobbler, mend my shoe,
Get it done by half past two;
Stitch it up, and stitch it down,
Then I'll give you half a crown.

Old King Cole

Old King Cole
    Was a merry old soul,
And a merry old soul was he;
    He called for his pipe,
        And he called for his bowl,
And he called for his fiddlers three.

Every fiddler he had a fiddle,
And a very fine fiddle had he;
Oh, there's none so rare
    As can compare
With King Cole and his fiddlers three.

Wooden Hill

Up the wooden hill
   to Bedfordshire,
Down Sheet Lane
   to Blanket Fair.

Curly Locks

Curly locks, Curly locks,
   Wilt thou be mine?
Thou shalt not wash dishes
   Nor yet feed the swine;
But sit on a cushion
   And sew a fine seam,
And feed upon strawberries,
   Sugar and cream.

Punctuality

First in a carriage,
Second in a gig,
Third on a donkey,
And fourth on a pig.

Harvest

The boughs do shake and the bells
    do ring,
So merrily comes our harvest in,
Our harvest in, our harvest in,
So merrily comes our harvest in.

We've ploughed, we've sowed,
We've reaped, we've mowed,
We've got our harvest in.

Betty Botter's Batter

Betty Botter bought some butter,
But, she said, the butter's bitter;
If I put it in my batter
It will make my batter bitter,
But a bit of better butter,
That would make my batter better.
So she bought a bit of butter
Better than her bitter butter,
And she put it in her batter
And the batter was not bitter.
So t'was better Betty Botter
Bought a bit of better butter.

Riddles

In marble walls as white as milk,
Lined with a skin as soft as silk,
Within a fountain crystal-clear,
A golden apple doth appear.
No doors there are to this stronghold,
Yet thieves break in and steal the gold.

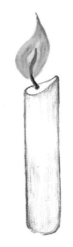

Little Nancy Etticoat,
With a white petticoat,
And a red nose;
She has no feet or hands,
The longer she stands
The shorter she grows.

In Spring I look gay,
Decked in comely array,
In Summer more clothing I wear;
When colder it grows,
I fling off my clothes,
And in Winter quite naked appear.

Two brothers we are,
Great burdens we bear,
On which we are bitterly pressed;
The truth is to say,
We are full all the day,
And empty when we go to rest.

I'm called by the name of a man;
Yet am as little as a mouse;
When winter comes I love to be
With my red target near the house.

Hickory, Dickory, Dock

Hickory, dickory, dock,
The mouse ran up the clock.
   The clock struck one,
   The mouse ran down,
Hickory, dickory, dock.